ASTRONAUTS
STICKER BOOK

Illustrated by Emi Ordás
Written by Struan Reid
Designed by Matt Preston
Consultant: Stuart Atkinson

CONTENTS

For links to websites with games and activities to find out more about astronauts, go to the Usborne Quicklinks Website at www.usborne.com/quicklinks and type in the title of this book. We recommend that children are supervised while using the internet.

You can find stickers to add to the pages
in the middle of this book.

EARLY SPACE SUITS

Astronauts need protective clothing to travel in space. In 1961, Yuri Gagarin of the Soviet Union became the first person to travel in space, in *Vostok 1*. He was followed one month later by United States astronaut Alan Shepard of the Mercury mission. By 1966, US Project Gemini had launched a total of 16 men into space.

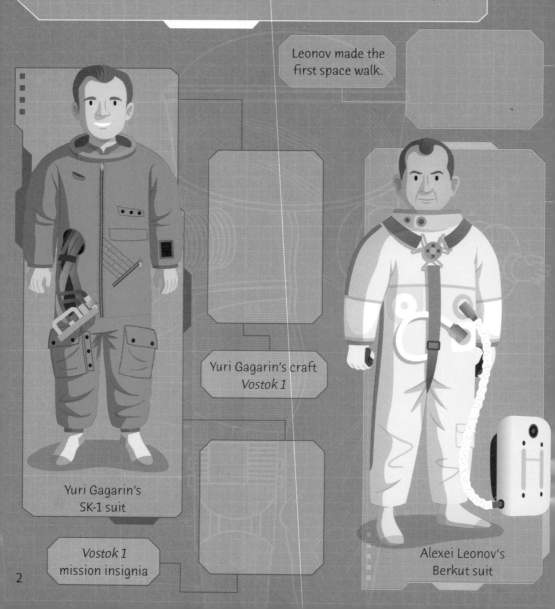

Leonov made the first space walk.

Yuri Gagarin's craft
Vostok 1

Yuri Gagarin's
SK-1 suit

Vostok 1
mission insignia

Alexei Leonov's
Berkut suit

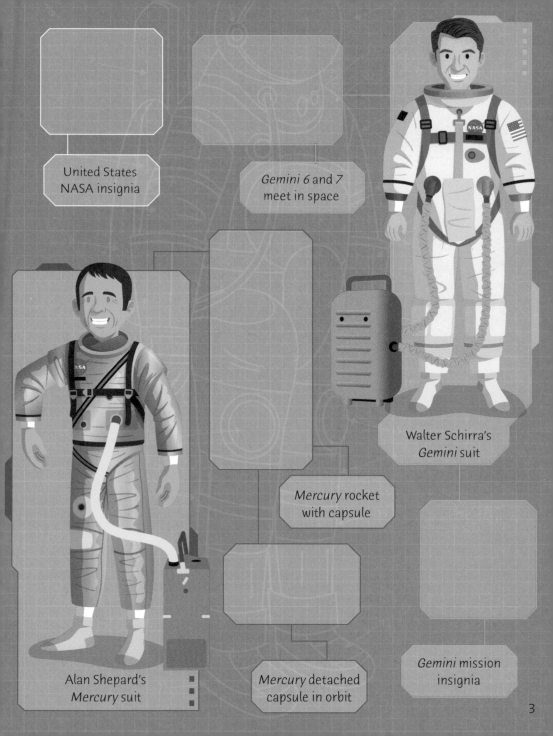

United States
NASA insignia

Gemini 6 and 7
meet in space

Walter Schirra's
Gemini suit

Alan Shepard's
Mercury suit

Mercury rocket
with capsule

Mercury detached
capsule in orbit

Gemini mission
insignia

3

WALKING ON THE MOON

The United States space program is run by the National Aeronautics and Space Administration (NASA). It is July 21, 1969, and US astronauts Neil Armstrong and Edwin "Buzz" Aldrin have just stepped out of the Lunar Module Eagle to become the first humans to walk on the surface of the Moon.

Neil Armstrong

"Buzz" Aldrin

LUNAR ROVER

In 1971, US astronauts David Scott and James Irwin have made the fourth successful landing on the Moon. They're using a Lunar Rover Vehicle for the first time, and will spend three days driving around and collecting scientific material which they'll bring back to Earth for analysis.

David Scott in Rover 1

JET PACK ASTRONAUT

In 1984, US astronaut Bruce McCandless is a crew member of a reusable spacecraft called Space Shuttle *Challenger*. He's making the first ever untethered spacewalk wearing a Manned Maneuvering Unit (MMU) on his back. Jet thrusters operated by hand controls allow him to move freely away from the Shuttle.

Bruce McCandless

SHUTTLE LANDING

The Space Shuttle has just landed back at base after a successful mission into space. The mission commander has stepped out in her bright orange landing gear and is heading for HQ, where she'll be debriefed and checked by doctors. Engineers will service the Shuttle so that it can be used to make more flights.

Mission commander

TRAINING UNDERWATER

Russian astronauts, known as cosmonauts, train with US astronauts in a water tank at the Neutral Buoyancy Laboratory (NBL) in the USA. This simulates the weightless conditions of space. They wear the same type of clothing and carry equipment similar to what they'll be using when they're in space.

Russian cosmonaut

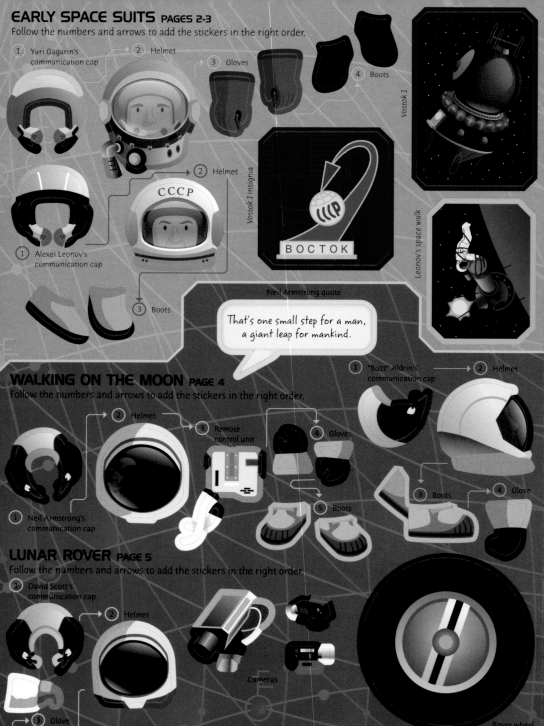

EARLY SPACE SUITS PAGES 2-3
Follow the numbers and arrows to add the stickers in the right order.

1. Yuri Gagarin's communication cap
2. Helmet
3. Gloves
4. Boots

Vostok 1

Vostok 1 insignia

BOCTOK

1. Alexei Leonov's communication cap
2. Helmet
3. Boots

Leonov's space walk

Neil Armstrong quote

That's one small step for a man, a giant leap for mankind.

WALKING ON THE MOON PAGE 4
Follow the numbers and arrows to add the stickers in the right order.

1. Neil Armstrong's communication cap
2. Helmet
3. Remote control unit
4. Gloves
5. Boots

1. "Buzz" Aldrin's communication cap
2. Helmet
3. Boots
4. Glove

LUNAR ROVER PAGE 5
Follow the numbers and arrows to add the stickers in the right order.

1. David Scott's communication cap
2. Helmet
3. Glove

Cameras

Rover wheel

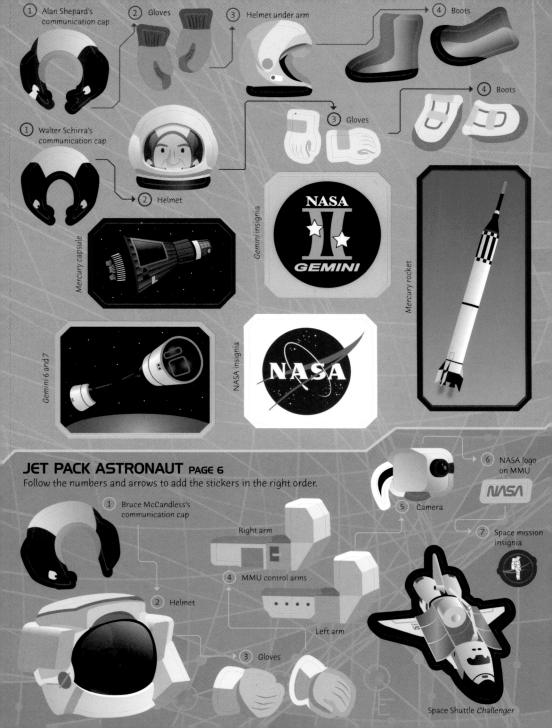

① Alan Shepard's communication cap

② Gloves

③ Helmet under arm

④ Boots

④ Boots

③ Gloves

① Walter Schirra's communication cap

② Helmet

Mercury capsule

Gemini insignia

NASA
II
GEMINI

Mercury rocket

Gemini 6 and 7

NASA insignia

NASA

JET PACK ASTRONAUT PAGE 6
Follow the numbers and arrows to add the stickers in the right order.

① Bruce McCandless's communication cap

Right arm

⑥ NASA logo on MMU

NASA

⑤ Camera

⑦ Space mission insignia

④ MMU control arms

② Helmet

Left arm

③ Gloves

Space Shuttle *Challenger*

SHUTTLE LANDING PAGE 7

Follow the numbers and arrows to add the stickers in the right order.

1 Mission commander's boots

2 Landing suit

TRAINING UNDERWATER PAGES 8-9

Follow the numbers and arrows to add the stickers in the right order.

1 Cosmonaut's Orlan suit

2 Electric drill

3 Electric saw

REDUCED GRAVITY
PAGES 12-13

Follow the numbers to add the stickers in the right order.

1 South Korean astronaut's shoes

2 Training suit

3 Identity tag

Water bottle

Apple

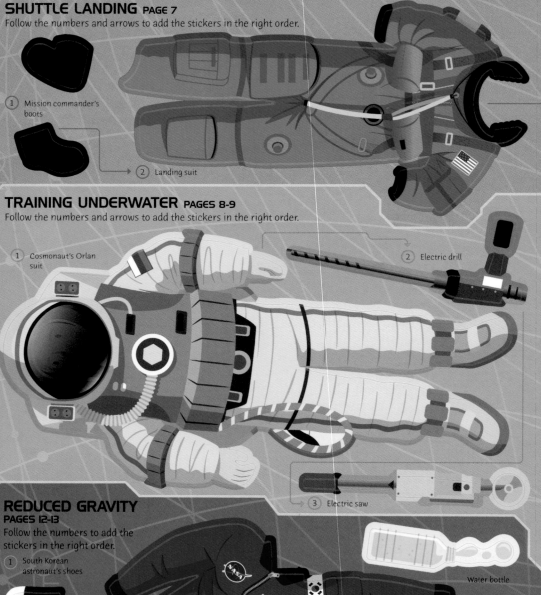

SPACE WALK PAGES 12-13

Follow the numbers and arrows to add the stickers in the right order.

1 Swedish astronaut's communication cap

2 Gloves

3 Helmet

4 Remote control unit on chest

5 Tool & harness

6 Tools

7 Camera

INSIDE THE ISS PAGES 14-15

Follow the numbers and arrows to add the stickers in the right order.

1 Exercising astronaut's shoes

2 Shorts

3 T-shirt

4 Knee pads

5 Waist harness

6 Safety harness down leg

Tool

1 Relaxing astronaut's socks

2 Shoes

3 Shorts

4 T-shirt

5 Guitar

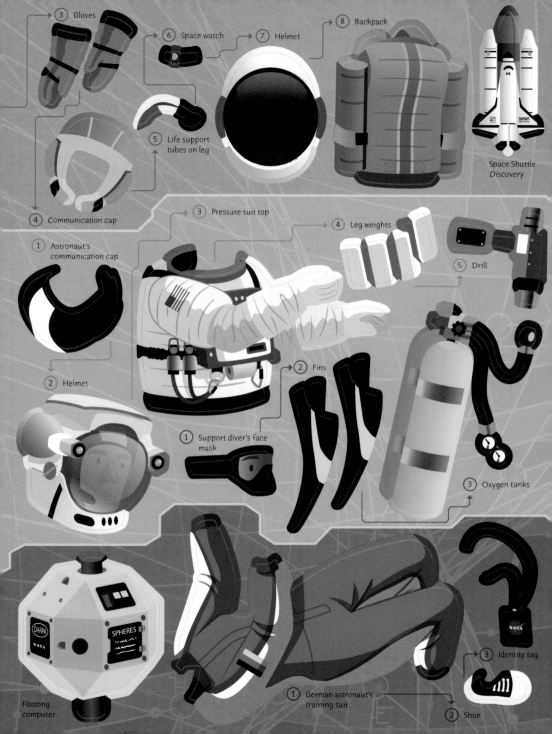

(3) Gloves

(6) Space watch → (7) Helmet

(8) Backpack

(5) Life support tubes on leg

Space Shuttle
Discovery

(4) Communication cap

(3) Pressure suit top

(4) Leg weights

(5) Drill

(1) Astronaut's communication cap

(2) Helmet

(2) Fins

(1) Support diver's face mask

(3) Oxygen tanks

Floating computer

(3) Identity tag

(1) German astronaut's training suit

(2) Shoe

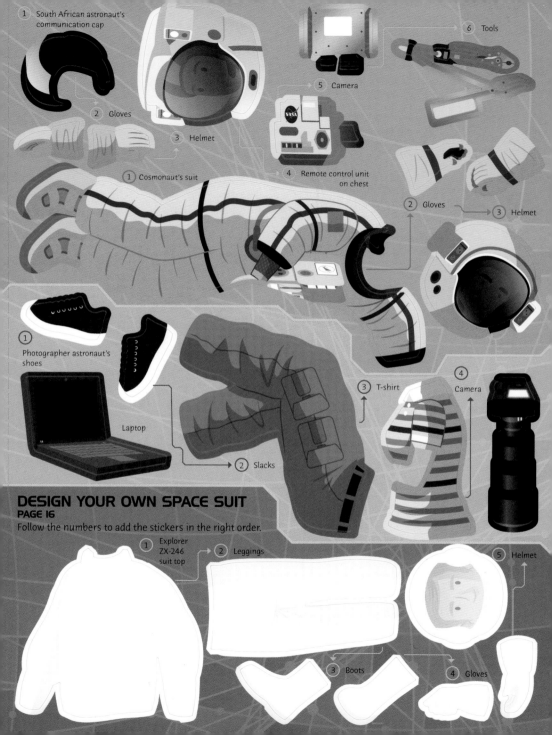

1 South African astronaut's communication cap

2 Gloves

3 Helmet

5 Camera

6 Tools

NASA

4 Remote control unit on chest

1 Cosmonaut's suit

2 Gloves

3 Helmet

1 Photographer astronaut's shoes

Laptop

3 T-shirt

4 Camera

2 Slacks

DESIGN YOUR OWN SPACE SUIT
PAGE 16
Follow the numbers to add the stickers in the right order.

1 Explorer ZX-246 suit top

2 Leggings

5 Helmet

3 Boots

4 Gloves

Support diver

US astronaut

REDUCED GRAVITY

One key stage in space training takes place in an aircraft. The plane flies up steeply and then drops down again, making the astronauts feel nearly weightless for 30 seconds at a time. This is known as reduced gravity training. They carry out some of the tasks that they'll perform when they're in space.

Padded walls

British astronaut

Floating computer

Trainer

10

South Korean astronaut turning somersaults

German astronaut

Floating balls

Computer equipment

11

SPACE WALK

Astronauts are carrying out checks and repairs to the outside of the
International Space Station (ISS). They're wearing jet packs known as SAFER
units. These can be used in emergencies, just in case they break away from
their tethers and float off into space.

Swedish
astronaut

Canadarm2
robot

Platform
controller

Russian
cosmonaut

Tether

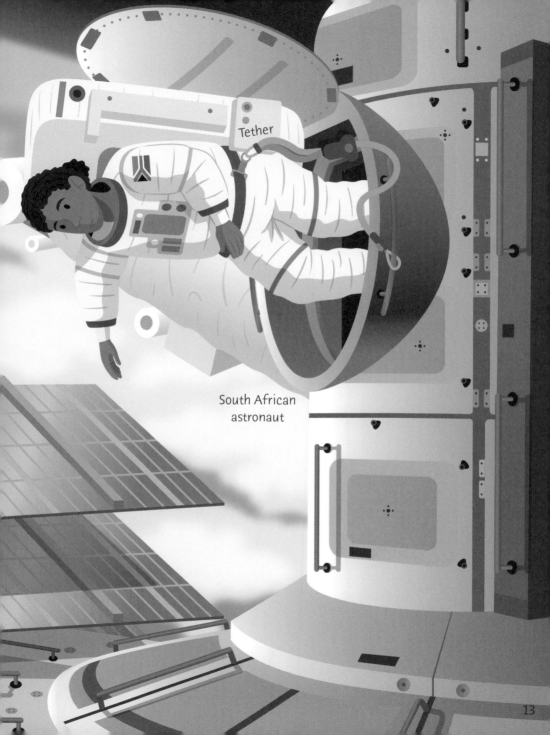

Tether

South African
astronaut

INSIDE THE ISS

These astronauts are inside the International Space Station (ISS). They can wear their everyday clothes inside, but with low gravity their living conditions are very different from those back home. In between their daily scientific tasks and their hobbies, they have to keep fit while on board.

Doing exercise

Doing photography

EXIT

Relaxing

15

DESIGN YOUR OWN SPACE SUIT

You've seen what people wear in space, now it's your turn to design your own space suits. You can use the suits you've seen in this book as inspiration for your own design. Use felt-tip pens for the Space Explorer on the left and the stickers at the end of this book for the Explorer on the right.

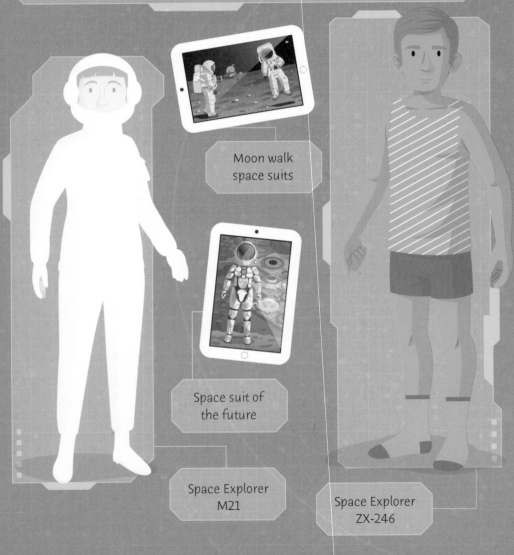

Moon walk
space suits

Space suit of
the future

Space Explorer
M21

Space Explorer
ZX-246